WORKING WITH
ANALOGIES
Making Connections
BOOK 1

Written by Jim McAlpine, Betty Weincek,
Sue Jeweler, and Marion Finkbinder
Illustrated by Karen Birchak

ISBN 1-56644-129-3

© 2004 Educational Impressions, Inc.

PRINTED IN THE U.S.A.

EDUCATIONAL IMPRESSIONS, INC.
Hawthorne, New Jersey 07507

Table of Contents

Introduction to the Teacher

Understanding and decoding analogies is a skill that is transferable to reading comprehension, critical thinking, and creativity. Analogies can be expressed in visual, symbolic, numerical, verbal, and inferential terms. Analogies help students develop the ability to make and appreciate connections between and among a variety of stimuli.

As students become more adept at using, creating, and deciphering analogies, the process of transferring and expressing the inherent nature of analogies becomes a "thinking game" for them. The game can be successfully played at almost any level of thinking. The use of analogy-based thinking can then be applied effectively to thinking about ideas and concepts in the array of facts, terms, and information presented throughout the various curricula students encounter at any grade in school.

RELATIONSHIPS

This book is divided into five main sections based upon the type of relationship described by the analogies in it: Part to Whole / Whole to Part; Synonyms / Antonyms; Cause to Effect / Effect to Cause; Purpose, Use or Function; and Degree.

- **Part to Whole / Whole to Part**
  The analogies in this section describe the relationship between a thing and a piece or building block of that thing and vice versa.

- **Synonyms / Antonyms**
  The analogies in this section describe the relationship between a thing and something that is similar in meaning (Synonym) or a thing and something that is opposite in meaning (Antonym).

- **Cause to Effect / Effect to Cause**
  The analogies in this section describe the relationship between an event or happening and a resulting change or outcome and vice versa.

- **Purpose, Use or Function**
  The analogies in this section describe the relationship between an object or a concept and how it works or why it exists.

- **Degree**
  The analogies in this section describe the relationship between an object or an idea and the increasing or decreasing value of that object or idea.

FORMAT

Each section of the book includes a definition of the relationship featured in the section, an example of the type of analogy, and three levels of practice: Practice with Choices, Open-ended Practice, and Create Your Own. The Create-Your-Own portion provides an opportunity for students to create new analogies that fit the construct of the section. Extensions, found at the end of each section, and Connectics, found at the end of the unit, provide opportunities for creative word play.

- **Definition of the Analogy**
  A general definition is given for each type of analogy. Allow your students some leeway regarding the definition when they do the open-ended exercises and when creating original analogies. Students should be encouraged to stretch their imaginations; however, they should be required to justify why the analogy fits.

- **Example**
  An example of the analogy is given. This example will closely fit the definition.

- **Practice with Choices**
  These exercises introduce the structure and operation of analogies. They present a nearly completed analogy with options given. Students will test or try as many as necessary in order to complete the analogy successfully. Instruct them to stretch their imaginations. If no answer fits even then, the correct answer may be "none of the above."

- **Open-ended Practice**
  These exercises extend and expand the understanding of analogies. In these exercises part of each analogy is left out and students must determine an appropriate option to complete it. Students must justify their solutions.

- **Create Your Own! ***
  These exercises further deepen the understanding and operation of analogies. Various portions of 4-part analogies are given. Students must generate a complete analogy for each and should be encouraged to stretch their imagination and use their creativity. They must justify their solutions.

- **Extensions and Connectics**
  These exercises encourage students to create connections to word play and depth of meaning. While they are not analogies, they are meant to be an outgrowth of the vocabulary kids learn and use by doing the analogies.

* An important objective of the Open-ended Practice and Create-Your-Own exercises is for students to go beyond the obvious analogies and to create justifiable analogies that will challenge the thinking skills of their peers.

PRESENTATION OF ANALOGIES

Each section includes both visual/symbolic and verbal analogies. The verbal analogies are presented in an interdisciplinary format and include language arts, science, social studies, math, and the arts.

- **Visual / Symbolic**
  These analogies use pictorial representations of objects and concepts.

- **Verbal**
  These analogies use words to represent objects and ideas.

- **Interdisciplinary**
  Interdisciplinary is defined as a concept view and curriculum approach that deliberately applies a variety of methodology and language from an array of discipline fields to examine a theme, a problem, an issue, an experience, or a topic. An interdisciplinary approach integrates thinking and learning skills and unifies content and process. Students are provided with a range of stimulating and motivating curriculum experiences that engage them in thoughtful confrontation with subject matter while fostering abstract thinking.

CORRELATION TO BLOOM'S TAXONOMY

- **Definitions, Examples and Structured Practice**
  These mirror the knowledge, comprehension, application, and analysis levels of thinking in Bloom's Taxonomy.

- **Open-Ended Practice, Create-Your-Own Practice and Extensions**
  These challenge the student to use the higher-level thinking skills of analysis, synthesis, and evaluation.

HOW TO USE THIS BOOK

This book is structured to go from concrete to abstract thinking in logical, sequential steps. Successful use of this book requires direct instruction through each step of the process, in the order given.

1. Introduction to Analogies

2. Simulation (Examples)

3. Simple Practice

4. Advanced Practice

5. Open-Ended Practice

6. Create-Your-Own Practice

7. Application and Extension

At each step of the process, students may be grouped in any of the following ways:

• Whole Group

• Small Group

• Individual

• Pair / Share

• Group / Share

• Pair / Solve

The purpose for using the analogy activities may include, but is not limited to, the following:

• Warm-up

• Vocabulary Development

• Comprehension

• Content Extension

• Critical and Creative Thinking

Introduction for Kids

An analogy is a thinking puzzle. It shows the relationship of one thing to another. Analogies can be pictures, symbols, words, numbers, or ideas. Analogies are fun!

Analogies can help you…

- stretch your thinking

- increase your vocabulary

- enjoy word play

- learn and use many word meanings

- improve your analysis skills

- see things in new and different ways

An analogy is a kind of sentence. It includes four parts, or items. In a successful analogy, the first two items have a relationship. The last two items have a relationship that parallels the first relationship. The completed analogy can be read like a sentence.

EXAMPLE
You have four items.
    Item A: Big
    Item B: Large
    Item C: Little
    Item D: Small

The analogy may be written as A : B :: C : D.
The completed analogy reads like a sentence:
    Item A (Big) is to Item B (Large) as Item C (Little) is to Item D (Small).

EXPLANATION:
Big and *Large* are synonyms. *Little* and *Small* are also synonyms.

The analogy may also be written as A : C :: B : D.
The completed analogy reads like a sentence:
    Item A (Big) is to Item C (Little) as Item B (Large) is to Item D (Small).

EXPLANATION:
Big and *Little* are antonyms. *Large* and *Small* are also antonyms.

HOW TO SOLVE AN ANALOGY

1. Look at the items given.

2 Consider any obvious relationships between the items.

3. Predict possible answers that would fit any of the relationships you considered.

OR

Look at the possible answers and analyze which one may be correct.

4. Test the analogy sentence by reading it. "*Big* is to *large* as *little* is to *small*."

5. See if the analogy works.

6. Return to Step #1 if necessary.

REMEMBER the two elements (items) on the left side of the double colon in an analogy must have the same relationship as the two elements (items) on the right side of the double colon. The relationship and the analogy must be balanced and logical.

WHAT'S INSIDE THIS BOOK!

Activities include the following sections:

- **Part to Whole / Whole to Part**
  The analogies in this section describe the relationship between a thing and a piece or building block of that thing and vice versa.

- **Synonyms / Antonyms**
  The analogies in this section describe the relationship between a thing and something that is similar in meaning (Synonym) or a thing and something that is opposite in meaning (Antonym).

- **Cause to Effect / Effect to Cause**
  The analogies in this section describe the relationship between an event or happening and a resulting change or outcome or vice versa.

- **Purpose, Use or Function**
  The analogies in this section describe the relationship between an object or a concept and how it works or why it exists.

- **Degree**
  The analogies in this section describe the relationship between an object or an idea and the increasing or decreasing value of that object or idea.

Each section is divided into:

- **Definition**

- **Example**

- **Practice with Choices**

- **Open-Ended Practice**

- **Create-Your-Own Practice**

- **Extensions!**

Each section includes analogies that are:

- **Visual / Symbolic (Picture Representations)**

- **Verbal (Involving or Having to Do with Words)**

- **Interdisciplinary (Involving or Having to Do with School Subjects)**

Extensions! are opportunities for you to play with analogies. You get to invent, prove, create, and share the fun!

Connectics!, found at the end of the unit, provide additional creative word-play opportunities.

Part to Whole / Whole to Part

Definition:

THE RELATIONSHIP BETWEEN A PIECE OR BUILDING BLOCK
OF A LARGER THING AND THAT THING

Example:

PART TO WHOLE

page : book :: pane : window

WHOLE TO PART

tree : leaf :: class : student

Look at the first two items in the first analogy. A page is a part of a book. We say, therefore, that they have a part-to-whole relationship. Look at the last two items in the first analogy; they should have a similar relationship. A pane is a part of a window. They, too, have a part-to-whole relationship. The analogy works!

Now look at the first two items in the second analogy. The tree represents the whole. A leaf is part of that whole. We say, therefore, that they have a whole-to-part relationship. Look at the last two items in the second analogy; they should have a similar relationship. A student is a part of a class. They, too, have a whole-to-part relationship. The analogy works!

We can read the two analogies as sentences:

Page is to *book* as *pane* is to *window.*

Tree is to *leaf* as *class* is to *student.*

PRACTICE!

VISUAL AND SYMBOLIC
Practice with Choices

1. [quarter circle] : [circle divided in four] :: [rectangle] : _____

   a. [rectangle divided into four]   b. [circle]

   c. [chair]   d. none of the above

2. [circle] : [half circle open up] :: [rectangle] : _____

   a. [right angle with small square]   b. [half circle open left]

   c. [open rectangle bottom]   d. none of the above

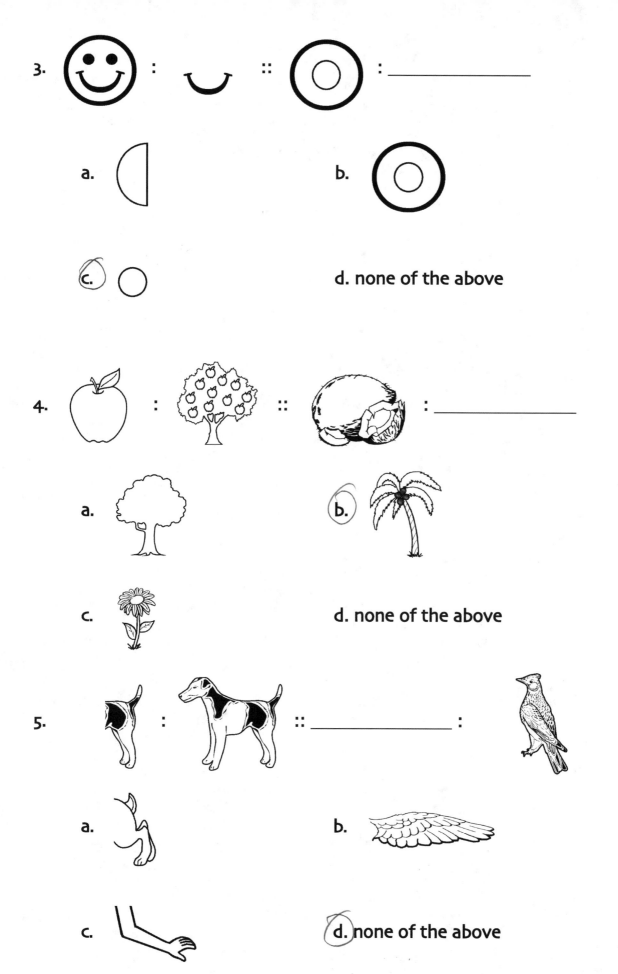

3.   :   ::   :_____

a.   b.

c.   d. none of the above

4.   :   ::   :_____

a.   b.

c.   d. none of the above

5.   :   :: _____ :

a.   b.

c.   d. none of the above

Open-Ended Practice

1. [lid] : [jar] :: [door] : <u>house</u>

2. [propeller] : [helicopter] :: <u>sail</u> : [sailboat]

3. [lamp] : [plug] :: [car] : <u>tires</u>

4. [ear] : [head] :: [finger] : <u>hand</u>

5. [button] : [jacket] :: [zipper] : _____

Create Your Own
Part-to-Whole and Whole-to-Part Analogies!

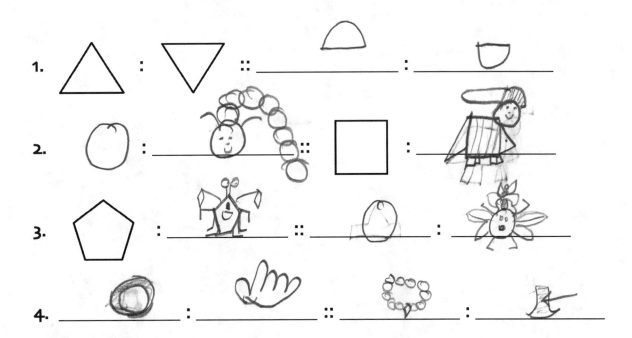

1. [triangle] : [inverted triangle] :: _____ : [bowl shape]

2. [oval] : _____ :: [square] : _____

3. [pentagon] : _____ :: _____ : _____

4. _____ : _____ :: _____ : _____

VERBAL (INTERDISCIPLINARY)
Practice with Choices

LANGUAGE ARTS

1. tree : treehouse :: back : _____

   a. backpack

   b. football

   c. shoe

   d. none of the above

2. verb : sentence :: vowel : _____

   a. paragraph

   b. word

   c. part of speech

   d. none of the above

3. chapter : novel :: sentence : _____

   a. phrase

   b. paragraph

   c. adverb

   d. none of the above

SOCIAL STUDIES

1. citizen : community :: kitten : _____

   a. pod

   b. litter

   c. crowd

   d. none of the above

2. city : state :: state : _____

   a. pack

   b. room

   c. nation

   d. none of the above

3. state : city :: city : _____

   a. continent

   b. state

   c. nation

   d. none of the above

SCIENCE

1. branch : tree :: stem : _____

    a. dog

    b. pickle

    c. plant

    d. none of the above

2. butterfly : wing :: flower : _____

    a. seed

    b. petal

    c. food

    d. none of the above

3. knee : leg :: elbow : _____

    a. hand

    b. arm

    c. neck

    d. none of the above

MATH

1. inch : foot :: minute : _____

    a. second

    b. hour

    c. yard

    d. none of the above

2. pint : quart :: quart : _____

    a. gallon

    b. ounce

    c. pinch

    d. none of the above

3. sixteen : two :: twenty-one : _____

    a. four

    b. seven

    c. nine

    d. none of the above

ARTS

1. red : rainbow :: blue : _____

    a. orange

    b. red

    c. yellow

    (d.) none of the above

2. pencil : lead :: paintbrush : _____

    (a.) bristles

    b. chalk

    c. painting

    d. none of the above

3. strings : guitar :: keys : _____

    a. trombone

    b. tambourine

    (c.) piano

    d. none of the above

Open-Ended and Create-Your-Own
Part-to-Whole
and Whole-to-Part Analogies!

LANGUAGE ARTS

1. book : jacket :: _____ : _____

2. couplet : quatrain :: _____ : _____

3. poem : _____ :: essay : _____

4. _____ : _____ :: _____ : _____

SOCIAL STUDIES

1. era : history :: _____ : _____

2. battle : _____ :: treaty : _____

3. culture: _____ :: _____ : _____

4. _____ : _____ :: _____ : _____

SCIENCE

1. pound : ounce :: _____ : _____

2. _____ : clock :: _____ : microscope

3. solar system: _____ :: _____ : _____

4. _____ : _____ :: _____ : _____

MATH

1. rectangle : square :: _____oval_____ : _____circle_____

2. centimeter : _____meter_____ :: ounce : _____pound_____

3. equation: _____ :: _____ : _____

4. _____ : _____ :: _____ : _____

ARTS

1. line : shape :: _____ : _____

2. _____ : orange :: _____ : purple

3. verse : _____ :: _____ : _____

4. _____ : _____ :: _____ : _____

Extensions!
Using the Analogies You Created!

1. Use the analogies you developed in this section to create similes and/or metaphors.

_____

_____

_____

_____

_____

2. Write a poem or story around one of the similes or metaphors that you created.

_____

_____

_____

_____

_____

3. Create an artistic expression of one of your analogies. Sketch your idea in the space below.

Synonyms / Antonyms

Definition:

THE RELATIONSHIP BETWEEN A THING AND SOMETHING THAT IS SIMILAR IN MEANING (SYNONYM) OR A THING AND SOMETHING THAT IS OPPOSITE IN MEANING (ANTONYM)

Example:

SYNONYMS

big : large :: little : small

ANTONYMS

big : small :: large : little

Look at the first two items in the first analogy. *Big* means the same as *large;* they are synonyms. Look at the last two items in the first analogy; they should have a similar relationship. *Little* means the same as *small.* They have the same relationship as the first two items. The analogy works!

Now look at the first two items in the second analogy. *Big* means the opposite of *small;* they are antonyms. Look at the last two items in the second analogy; they should have a similar relationship. *Large* means the opposite of *little.* They have the same relationship as the first two items. The analogy works!

We can read the two analogies as sentences:

Big is to *large* as *little* is to *small.*

Big is to *small* as *large* is to *little.*

PRACTICE!

VISUAL AND SYMBOLIC
Practice with Choices

1. : :: :

a.

b.

c.

d. none of the above

2. : ::  : _____

a.

b.

c.

d. none of the above

3. :  ::  : _____

a.

b.

c.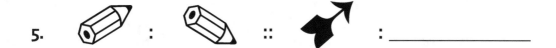

d. none of the above

4.  :  ::  : _____

a.

b.

c.

d. none of the above

5.

a.

b.

c.

d. none of the above

Open-Ended Practice

1.   : _____

2. X : **X** :: **+** : _____

3.   : _____

4. : :: : _____

5. -3 : +3 :: -7 : _____

Create Your Own
Synonym and Antonym Analogies!

1. ♥ : ♥ :: _____ : _____

2. **+** : _____ :: X : _____

3. 1/2 : 6/12 :: _____ : _____

4. _____ : _____ :: _____ : _____

VERBAL (INTERDISCIPLINARY)
Practice with Choices

LANGUAGE ARTS

1. true : false :: real : _____

    a. non-fiction

    b. movie

    c. pretend

    d. none of the above

2. out : in :: up : _____

    a. duck

    b. down

    c. sideways

    d. none of the above

3. answer : question :: synonym : _____

    a. phrase

    b. antonym

    c. reply

    d. none of the above

SOCIAL STUDIES

1. order : chaos :: law : _____

    a. police

    b. carnival

    c. rule

    d. none of the above

2. right : wrong :: innocent : _____

    a. nice

    b. mean

    c. guilty

    d. none of the above

3. rich : poor :: wealth : _____

    a. poverty

    b. riches

    c. evil

    d. none of the above

SCIENCE

1. sunrise : sunset :: noon : _____

    a. twilight

    b. dawn

    c. midnight

    d. none of the above

2. egg : seed :: arm : _____

    a. limb

    b. leaf

    c. eyelash

    d. none of the above

3. soft : loud :: light : _____

    a. fire

    b. heavy

    c. warmth

    d. none of the above

MATH

1. $7 - 3 = 4 : 4 + 3 = 7 ::$ subtraction : _____

    a. division

    b. multiplication

    c. addition

    d. none of the above

2. $3 + 3 = 6 :$ sum $:: 6 - 3 = 3 :$ _____

    a. difference

    b. product

    c. quotient

    d. none of the above

3. eighteen : eight plus ten :: ten : _____

    a. five plus six

    b. nine plus two

    c. twenty minus ten

    d. none of the above

ARTS

1. red : green :: blue : _____

    a. brown

    b. orange

    c. yellow

    d. none of the above

2. turn : pirouette :: _____ : leap

    a. stomp

    b. skip

    c. jump

    d. none of the above

3. sketch : erase :: paint : _____

    a. copy

    b. sketch

    c. draw

    d. none of the above

Open-Ended and Create-Your-Own Synonym and Antonym Analogies!

LANGUAGE ARTS

1. here : _____ :: _____ : _____

2. energetic : _____ :: lazy : _____

3. novel : _____ :: _____ : _____

4. _____ : _____ :: _____ : _____

SOCIAL STUDIES

1. rights : responsibilities :: _____ : _____

2. street : _____ :: avenue : _____

3. rich: _____ :: _____ : _____

4. _____ : _____ :: _____ : _____

SCIENCE

1. cloudy : sunny :: _____ : _____

2. mammal : _____ :: reptile : _____

3. fossil : _____ :: _____ : _____

4. _____ : _____ :: _____ : _____

MATH

1. odd : even :: _____ : _____

2. add : _____ :: multiply : _____

3. thirty-six : _____ :: _____ : _____

4. _____ : _____ :: _____ : _____

ARTS

1. classical : hip-hop :: _____ : _____

2. clap : applaud :: _____ : _____

3. chorus : _____ :: _____ : _____

4. _____ : _____ :: _____ : _____

Extensions!
Using the Analogies You Created!

1. Use the analogies you developed in this section to create similes and/or metaphors.

_____

_____

_____

_____

2. Write a poem or story around one of the similes or metaphors that you created.

_____

_____

_____

_____

_____

3. Create an artistic expression of one of your analogies. Sketch your idea in the space below.

Cause to Effect / Effect to Cause

Definition:

THE RELATIONSHIP BETWEEN AN EVENT OR HAPPENING
AND A RESULTING CHANGE OR OUTCOME OR VICE VERSA

Example:

CAUSE TO EFFECT

rain : flood :: snow : avalanche

EFFECT TO CAUSE

success : work :: tears : sadness

Look at the first two items in the first analogy. Rain causes a flood. Look at the last two items in the first analogy; they should have a similar relationship as the first two items. Snow causes an avalanche. Snow and avalanche have the same relationship as the first two items. The analogy works!

Now look at the first two items in the second analogy. Success is a result, or effect, of work. Look at the last two items in the second analogy; they should have a similar relationship as the first two items. Tears are a result, or effect, of sadness. Tears and sadness have the same relationship as the first two items. The analogy works!

We can read the two analogies as sentences:

Rain is to *flood* as *snow* is to *avalanche.*

Success is to *work* as *tears* is to *sadness.*

PRACTICE!

VISUAL AND SYMBOLIC
Practice with Choices

1.  :  ::  : _____

   a.    b.

   c.    d. none of the above

2. : ::  : _____

   a.    b.

   c.    d. none of the above

3.    : :: : _____

a.    b.

c.   d. none of the above

4.  :  ::  : _____

a.    b.

c.    d. none of the above

5. : :: : _____

a.    b.

c.    d. none of the above

Open-Ended Practice

1.  :  ::  : _____

2. : ::  : _____

3. : :: : _____

4.  :  ::  : _____

5. : : :: : _____

Create Your Own
Cause-and-Effect Analogies!

1. **7 + 1** : **8** :: _____ : _____

2. **6** : **10 - 4** :: _____ : _____

3. : _____ :: _____ : _____

4. _____ : _____ :: _____ : _____

         Working with Analogies: Book 1

VERBAL (INTERDISCIPLINARY)
Practice with Choices

LANGUAGE ARTS

1. joke : laughter :: tragedy : _____

   a. smirk

   b. gurgles

   c. tears

   d. none of the above

2. teaching : learning :: practice : _____

   a. answers

   b. improve

   c. lazy

   d. none of the above

3. study : learn :: memorize : _____

   a. remember

   b. fail

   c. read

   d. none of the above

SOCIAL STUDIES

1. traffic : congestion :: red light : _____

   a. stop

   b. slow down

   c. reverse

   d. none of the above

2. conflict : war :: agreement : _____

   a. tie

   b. peace

   c. stalemate

   d. none of the above

3. practice : win :: steal : _____

   a. agreement

   b. award

   c. jail

   d. none of the above

SCIENCE

1. cold : freeze :: warm : _____

   a. boil

   b. melt

   c. rough

   d. none of the above

2. swan : cygnet :: dog : _____

   a. beagle

   b. puppy

   c. kitten

   d. none of the above

3. itch : scratch :: hunger : _____

   a. eat

   b. drink

   c. walk

   d. none of the above

MATH

1. add : more than :: subtract : _____

    a. less than

    b. more than

    c. same as

    d. none of the above

2. add : sum :: subtract : _____

    a. difference

    b. product

    c. quotient

    d. none of the above

3 multiply : product :: divide : _____

    a. difference

    b. product

    c. quotient

    d. none of the above

ARTS

1. harden clay : pottery :: chisel stone : _____

    a. statue

    b. collage

    c. mobile

    d. none of the above

2. sound : violin :: tap : _____

    a. meter

    b. ballet

    c. shoe

    d. none of the above

3. Academy Award : great movie :: Olympic medal : _____

    a. great athletic performance

    b. poor athletic performance

    c. perfect attendance

    d. none of the above

Open-Ended and Create-Your-Own Cause-to-Effect and Effect-to-Cause Analogies!

LANGUAGE ARTS

1. mistakes : erase :: _____ : _____

2. studying : _____ :: laziness : _____

3. write : _____ :: _____ : _____

4. _____ : _____ :: _____ : _____

SOCIAL STUDIES

1. problem : thinking :: _____ : _____

2. highways : _____ :: railroads : _____

3. rescue : _____ :: _____ : _____

4. _____ : _____ :: _____ : _____

SCIENCE

1. earthquake : destruction :: _____ : _____

2. bake : _____ :: build : _____

3. pupa : _____ :: _____ : _____

4. _____ : _____ :: _____ : _____

MATH

1. flash cards : learn facts :: _____ : _____

2. length x width : area :: _____ : _____

3. 2 x 1 pint : _____ :: 4 x 1 quart : _____

4. _____ : _____ :: _____ : _____

ARTS

1. award : pride :: _____ : _____

2. appreciate : applause :: _____ : _____

3. doodle : _____ :: _____ : _____

4. _____ : _____ :: _____ : _____

Extensions!
Using the Analogies You Created!

1. Use the analogies you developed in this section to create similes and/or metaphors.

_____

_____

_____

_____

_____

2. Write a poem or story around one of the similes or metaphors that you created.

_____

_____

_____

_____

_____

3. Create an artistic expression of one of your analogies. Sketch your idea in the space below.

PURPOSE, USE OR FUNCTION

Definition:

THE RELATIONSHIP BETWEEN AN OBJECT OR A CONCEPT
AND HOW IT WORKS OR WHY IT EXISTS

Example:

hangar : planes :: garage : cars

Look at the first two items in the analogy. The purpose of a hangar is to house airplanes. Look at the last two items in the analogy; they should have a similar relationship. The purpose of a garage is to house cars. Garage and cars have the same relationship as the first two items. The analogy works!

We can read the analogy as a sentence:

Hangar is to *planes* as *garage* is to *cars.*

PRACTICE!

VISUAL AND SYMBOLIC
Practice with Choices

1.   : :: : _____

a.

b.

c.

d. none of the above

2. : ::  : _____

a.

b.

c.

d. none of the above

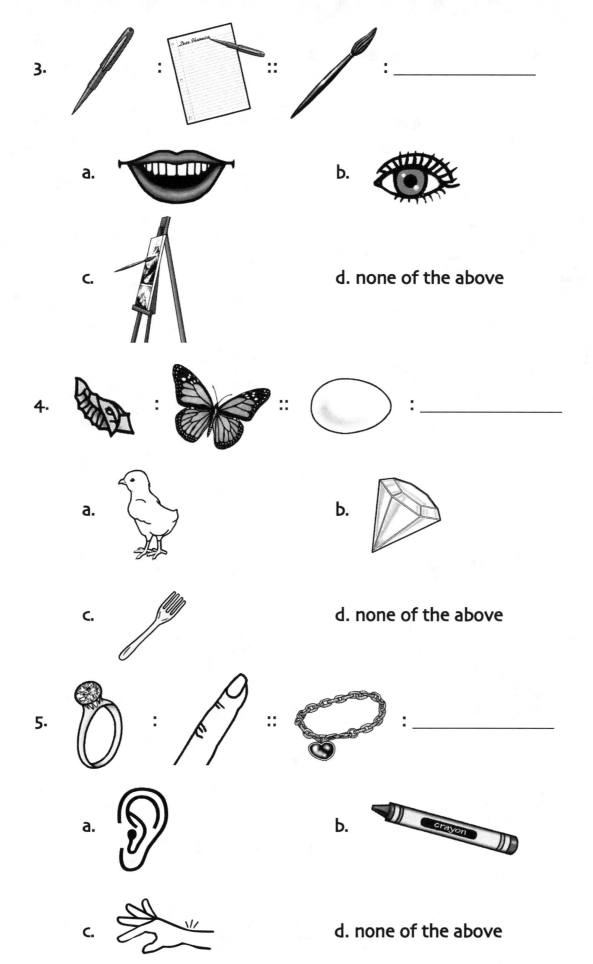

3.

a.

b.

c.

d. none of the above

4.

a.

b.

c.

d. none of the above

5.

a.

b.

c.

d. none of the above

Open-Ended Practice

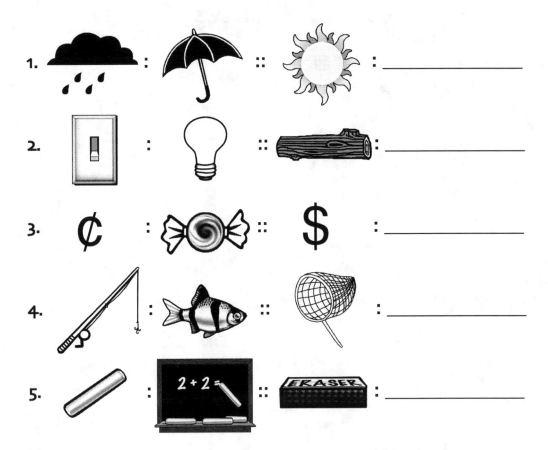

1. : :: : _____

2. : :: : _____

3. ¢ : :: $: _____

4. : :: : _____

5. : :: : _____

Create Your Own
Purpose, Use or Function Analogies!

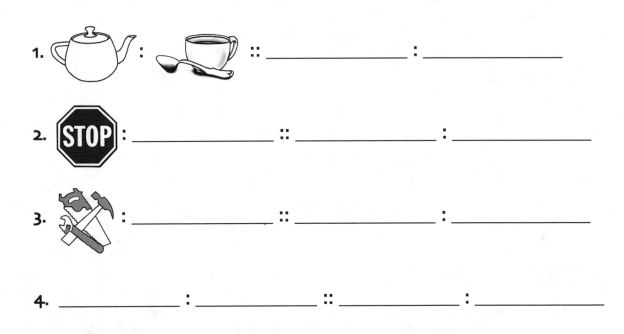

1. : :: _____ : _____

2. STOP : _____ :: _____ : _____

3. : _____ :: _____ : _____

4. _____ : _____ :: _____ : _____

VERBAL (INTERDISCIPLINARY)
Practice with Choices

LANGUAGE ARTS

1. verb : action :: noun: _____

    a. predicate

    b. thing

    c. modifier

    d. none of the above

2. adverb : verb :: adjective : _____

    a. noun

    b. conjunction

    c. preposition

    d. none of the above

3. period : stop :: comma : _____

    a. speed up

    b. emphasize

    c. pause

    d. none of the above

SOCIAL STUDIES

1. President : lead :: police officer : _____

    a. clean

    b. teach

    c. protect

    d. none of the above

2. law : regulate :: fine : _____

    a. cost

    b. punish

    c. reward

    d. none of the above

3. President : White House :: Congress : _____

    a. Lincoln Memorial

    b. Supreme Court

    c. Capitol

    d. none of the above

SCIENCE

1. water : power :: dynamite : _____

   a. excellent

   b. explosion

   c. powder

   d. none of the above

2. skeleton : human body :: stem : _____

   a. rhinoceros

   b. brain

   c. plant

   d. none of the above

3. oven : heat :: refrigerator : _____

   a. cook

   b. cool

   c. serve

   d. none of the above

MATH

1. dozen : twelve :: single : _____

    a. none

    b. one

    c. both

    d. none of the above

2. calculator : calculate :: ruler : _____

    a. measure

    b. mix

    c. draw

    d. none of the above

3. flash cards : practice :: quiz : _____

    a. test knowledge

    b. teach

    c. quotient

    d. none of the above

ARTS

1. paint : color :: yarn : _____

    a. cat

    b. spool

    c. texture

    d. none of the above

2. video : view :: CD : _____

    a. taste

    b. hear

    c. smell

    d. none of the above

3. book : read :: skit : _____

    a. perform

    b. write

    c. color

    d. none of the above

Open-Ended and Create-Your-Own
Purpose, Function or Use
Analogies!

LANGUAGE ARTS

1. period : stop :: _____ : _____

2. book : _____ :: bicycle : _____

3. sentence : _____ :: _____ : _____

4. _____ : _____ :: _____ : _____

SOCIAL STUDIES

1. road : travel :: _____ : _____

2. jail : prisoners :: _____ : _____

3. firefighter : _____ :: _____ : _____

4. _____ : _____ :: _____ : _____

SCIENCE

1. lungs : breathe :: _____ : _____

2. brain : _____ :: muscles : _____

3. oil : _____ :: water : _____

4. _____ : _____ :: _____ : _____

MATH

1. hour : 60 minutes :: _____ : _____

2. 36 inches : _____ :: _____ : _____

3. C : 100 :: _____ : _____

4. _____ : _____ :: _____ : _____

ARTS

1. crayon : draw :: _____ : _____

2. frame : _____ :: _____ : _____

3. quarter notes : _____ :: _____ : _____

4. _____ : _____ :: _____ : _____

Extensions!
Using the Analogies You Created!

1. Use the analogies you developed in this section to create similes and/or metaphors.

_____

_____

_____

_____

_____

2. Write a poem or story around one of the similes or metaphors that you created.

_____

_____

_____

_____

_____

_____

3. Create an artistic expression of one of your analogies. Sketch your idea in the space below.

DEGREE

Definition:

THE RELATIONSHIP BETWEEN AN OBJECT OR AN IDEA AND THE INCREASING OR DECREASING VALUE OF THAT OBJECT OR IDEA

Example:

DECREASING VALUE
black : grey :: red : pink

INCREASING VALUE
grey : black :: pink : red

Look at the first two items in the analogy. Grey is a decreasing value of black. Look at the last two items in the analogy; they should have a similar relationship. Pink is a decreasing value of red. They have the same relationship as the first two items. The analogy works!

Now look at the first two items in the second analogy. Black is an increasing value of grey. Look at the last two items in the analogy; they should have a similar relationship. Red is an increasing value of pink. They have the same relationship as the first two items. The analogy works!

We can read the two analogies as sentences:

Black is to *grey* as *red* is to *pink.*

Grey is to *black* as *pink* is to *red.*

PRACTICE!

VISUAL AND SYMBOLIC
Practice with Choices

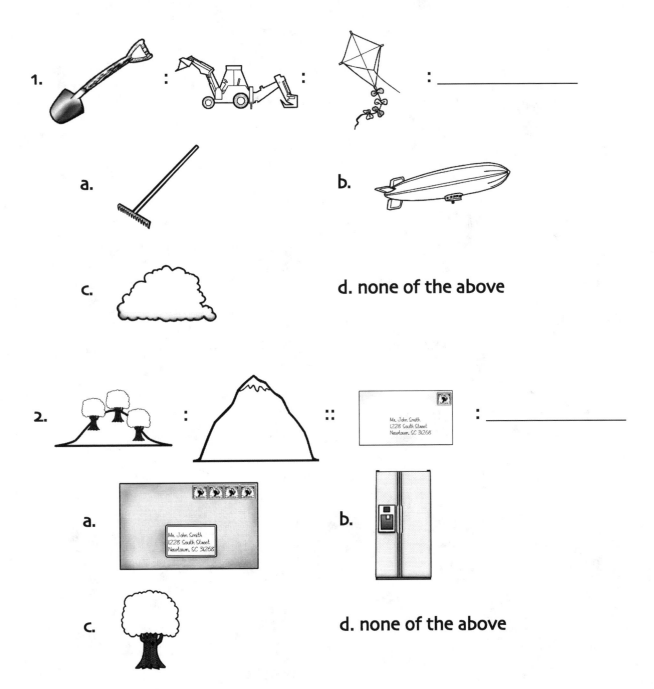

1. [shovel] : [backhoe] : [kite] : _____

a. [rake]

b. [blimp]

c. [cloud]

d. none of the above

2. [trees on hills] : [mountain] :: [envelope] : _____

a. [envelope with stamps]

b. [refrigerator]

c. [tree]

d. none of the above

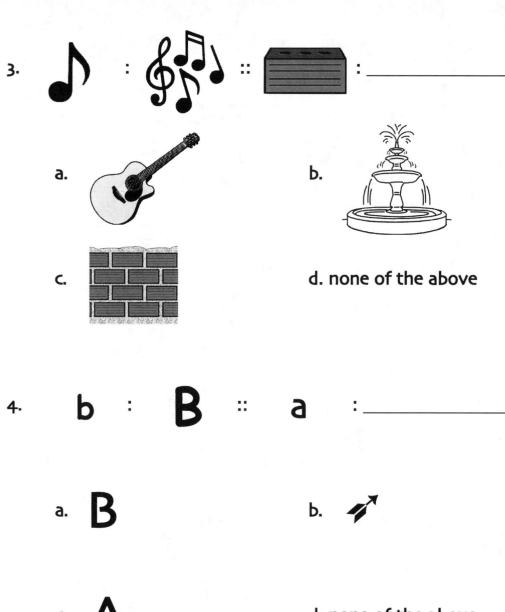

3. ♪ : 🎼 :: ▭ : _____

a.

b.

c.

d. none of the above

4. **b** : **B** :: **a** : _____

a. **B**

b.

c. **A**

d. none of the above

5. 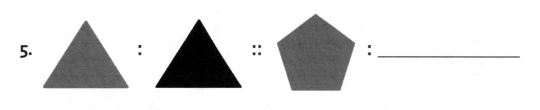 : :: : _____

a.

b.

c.

d. none of the above

Open-Ended Practice

1. ➤➤ : ➤➤➤ :: ➤↗ : _____

2. ☐ : ☐☐ :: ☐☐☐ : _____

3. △ : △ :: ☐ : _____

4. 🍦 : 🍦 :: _____ : _____

5. 🏠 : 🏰 :: 👶 : _____

Create Your Own
Purpose, Use or Function Analogies!

1. 🌳 : 🌲🌲 :: _____ : _____

2. 📖 : _____ :: 🖍 crayon : _____

3. 🕯 : _____ :: _____ : _____

4. _____ : _____ :: _____ : _____

VERBAL (INTERDISCIPLINARY)
Practice with Choices

LANGUAGE ARTS

1. we : me :: they : _____

    a. their

    b. she

    c. him

    d. none of the above

2. say : exclaim :: ask : _____

    a. beg

    b. refuse

    c. say

    d. none of the above

3. look : examine :: surprise : _____

    a. annoy

    b. please

    c. shock

    d. none of the above

SOCIAL STUDIES

1. like : love :: dislike : _____

    a. fear

    b. hate

    c. joy

    d. none of the above

2. cottage : mansion :: path : _____

    a. woods

    b. home

    c. highway

    d. none of the above

3. farm : garden :: battle : _____

    a. war

    b. argument

    c. amusement park

    d. none of the above

SCIENCE

1. drizzle : downpour :: flurry : _____

    a. flood

    b. raindrop

    c. blizzard

    d. none of the above

2. moisten : drench :: sip : _____

    a. swallow

    b. gulp

    c. cup

    d. none of the above

3. explosion : pop :: mountain : _____

    a. hill

    b. avalanche

    c. mudslide

    d. none of the above

MATH

1. less : least :: more : _____

    a. none

    b. most

    c. both

    d. none of the above

2. large : huge :: small : _____

    a. tiny

    b. big

    c. bad

    d. none of the above

3. four : sixteen :: five : _____

    a. five

    b. ten

    c. twenty-five

    d. none of the above

ARTS

1. beige : brown :: taupe : _____

    a. green

    b. black

    c. brown

    d. none of the above

2. song : opera :: skit : _____

    a. Broadway play

    b. monologue

    c. poem

    d. none of the above

3. giggle : laugh :: applause : _____

    a. clap

    b. standing ovation

    c. stomp

    d. none of the above

Open-Ended and Create-Your-Own
Purpose, Function or Use
Analogies!

LANGUAGE ARTS

1. good : better :: bad : _____

2. tall : _____ :: short : _____

3. letter : _____ :: _____ : _____

4. _____ : _____ :: _____ : _____

SOCIAL STUDIES

1. ocean liner : canoe :: jet plane : _____

2. law : _____ :: shoplifting : _____

3. discussion : _____ :: _____ : _____

4. _____ : _____ :: _____ : _____

SCIENCE

1. arid : _____ :: swamped : moist

2. heated : _____ :: cooled : _____

3. muscular : _____ :: _____ : _____

4. _____ : _____ :: _____ : _____

MATH

1. abundance : enough :: gigantic : _____

2. Big Ben : clock :: _____ : _____

3. double : _____ :: _____ : _____

4. _____ : _____ :: _____ : _____

ARTS

1. building : skyscraper :: _____ : _____

2. sketch : painting :: _____ : _____

3. melody : _____ :: _____ : _____

4. _____ : _____ :: _____ : _____

Extensions!
Using the Analogies You Created!

1. Use the analogies you developed in this section to create similes and/or metaphors.

_____

_____

_____

_____

_____

2. Write a poem or story around one of the similes or metaphors that you created.

_____

_____

_____

_____

_____

3. Create an artistic expression of one of your analogies. Sketch your idea in the space below.

Connectics!
Exploring Word Relationships!

1. Explore word relationships by connecting two seemingly unrelated words. Each word you add should connect the previous word to the following one. When done, you will have connected the first word with the last.

EXAMPLE:

hot   pickle

hot   french fries   ketchup   hamburger   pickle

Now Create your Own!

_____

_____

_____

2. Explore word relationships by connecting words with opposite meanings. Each word you add should connect the previous word to the following one. When done, you will have connected the first word with the last.

EXAMPLE:

hot   cold

hot   warm   cool   cold

Now Create your Own!

_____

_____

_____

3. Invent your own way to use and demonstrate analogies.

ANSWER
SECTION

PART TO WHOLE / WHOLE TO PART

VISUAL AND SYMBOLIC

Practice with Choices

1. a
2. c
3. c
4. b
5. b

Open-Ended and Create-Your-Own Practice

Answers will vary. Accept any answers that the students can justify. The analogies should not only work but also fit the relationship: part to whole or whole to part.

VERBAL (INTERDISCIPLINARY)

Language Arts

1. a
2. b
3. b

Social Studies

1. b
2. c
3. d

Science

1. c
2. b
3. b

Math

1. b
2. a
3. b

Arts

1. d
2. a
3. c

Open-Ended and Create-Your-Own Interdisciplinary Analogies

Answers will vary. Accept any answers that the students can justify. The analogies should not only work but also fit the relationship: part to whole or whole to part.

EXTENSIONS

Answers will vary.

SYNONYMS / ANTONYMS

VISUAL AND SYMBOLIC

Practice with Choices

1. a
2. b
3. a
4. b
5. a

Open-Ended and Create-Your-Own Practice

Answers will vary. Accept any answers that the students can justify. The analogies should not only work but also fit the relationship: synonyms or antonyms.

VERBAL (INTERDISCIPLINARY)

Language Arts

1. c
2. b
3. b

Social Studies

1. d
2. c
3. a

Science

1. c
2. a
3. b

Math

1. c
2. a
3. c

Arts

1. b
2. c
3. d

Open-Ended and Create-Your-Own Interdisciplinary Analogies

Answers will vary. Accept any answers that the students can justify. The analogies should not only work but also fit the relationship: synonyms or antonyms.

EXTENSIONS

Answers will vary.

CAUSE TO EFFECT / EFFECT TO CAUSE

VISUAL AND SYMBOLIC

Practice with Choices

1. b
2. a
3. b
4. a
5. c

Open-Ended and Create-Your-Own Practice

Answers will vary. Accept any answers that the students can justify. The analogies should not only work but also fit the relationship: cause to effect or effect to cause.

VERBAL (INTERDISCIPLINARY)

Language Arts

1. c
2. b
3. a

Social Studies

1. a
2. b
3. c

Science

1. b
2. b
3. a

Math

1. a
2. a
3. c

Arts

1. a
2. c
3. a

Open-Ended and Create-Your-Own Interdisciplinary Analogies

Answers will vary. Accept any answers that the students can justify. The analogies should not only work but also fit the relationship: cause to effect or effect to cause.

EXTENSIONS

Answers will vary.

PURPOSE, USE OR FUNCTION

VISUAL AND SYMBOLIC

Practice with Choices

1. c
2. b
3. c
4. a
5. c

Open-Ended and Create-Your-Own Practice

Answers will vary. Accept any answers that the students can justify. The analogies should not only work but also fit the relationship: purpose, use or function.

VERBAL (INTERDISCIPLINARY)

Language Arts

1. b
2. a
3. c

Social Studies

1. c
2. b
3. c

Science

1. b
2. c
3. b

Math

1. b
2. a
3. a

Arts

1. c
2. b
3. a

Open-Ended and Create-Your-Own Interdisciplinary Analogies

Answers will vary. Accept any answers that the students can justify. The analogies should not only work but also fit the relationship: purpose, use or function.

EXTENSIONS

Answers will vary.

DEGREE
VISUAL AND SYMBOLIC
Practice with Choices

1. b
2. a
3. c
4. c
5. b

Open-Ended and Create-Your-Own Practice
Answers will vary. Accept any answers that the students can justify. The analogies should not only work but also fit the relationship: degree.

VERBAL (INTERDISCIPLINARY)
Language Arts

1. b
2. a
3. c

Social Studies

1. b
2. c
3. b

Science

1. c
2. b
3. a

Math

1. b
2. a
3. c

Arts

1. c
2. a
3. b

Open-Ended and Create-Your-Own Interdisciplinary Analogies
Answers will vary. Accept any answers that the students can justify. The analogies should not only work but also fit the relationship: degree.

EXTENSIONS
Answers will vary.
CONNECTICS
Answers will vary.